Ben Bear's Pot of Gold

Written and Illustrated
by
Sue Camm

BRIMAX BOOKS · NEWMARKET · ENGLAND

Ben, the little brown bear, wants to go out to play. "You cannot go out in the rain," says Mother Bear. She looks to see if the clouds have gone away. "Ben!" she says. "Look at the rainbow in the sky." The rainbow goes all the way to the Misty Hills. It ends at a tall pine tree.

"There is a story about a rainbow," says Mother Bear. "At the end of a rainbow there is a pot of gold." "Our rainbow ends at the tall pine tree," says Ben. "What fun! I can go to look for gold in the Misty Hills. I can look for it by the tall pine tree."

Ben sets off with a picnic box. It is full of good things to eat.

"Hello! Are you going to have a picnic?" says Bob the beaver.

"No," says Ben. "I am off to the Misty Hills. I want to find the pot of gold at the end of the rainbow."

"I will come too!" says Bob.

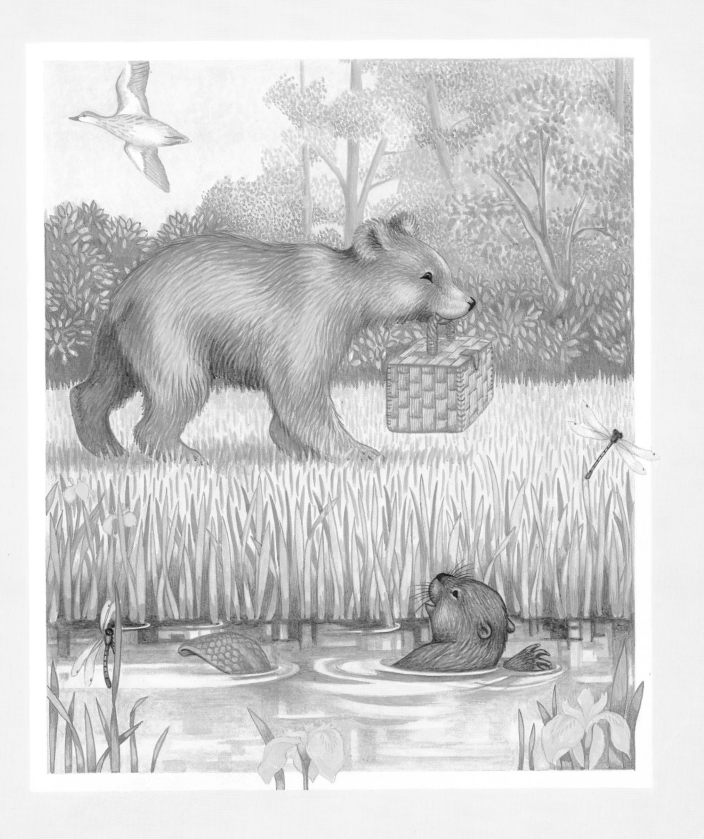

Ben and Bob set off down
the path. They meet
Skipper the chipmunk.
"We are on our way to the
Misty Hills," says Ben.
"There is a pot of gold
at the end of the rainbow.
We are going to find it,
by the tall pine tree."
"What fun!" says Skipper.
"Wait for me,
I will come too!"

Ben, Bob and Skipper
follow the path to the
Misty Hills.
"We are off to look for
gold by the tall pine
tree," sings Ben.
"We will find the pot
of gold," sings Bob.
Meg the magpie hears them.
"What fun!" she says.
                    "Wait for me,
                    I will come too!"

It is a very long way
to the Misty Hills.
They stop at a pond to
drink. Bob the beaver
has a swim.
"This is a lovely pond to
swim in," he says.
"Swimming is what I like
to do best of all."
"We can call it Bob's Pond,"
says Ben. "But
now we must go."

They have a long way to go
so they rest in the forest.
Skipper finds an old log.
"This would make a lovely
house," he says.
"The best kind of house
for a chipmunk is inside
an old log."
"We can call it Skipper's
Log," says Ben.
                    "But now we
                    must go on."

They all go along the path
to the Misty Hills.
"Where is Meg the magpie?"
"Here I am," says Meg.
"Look what I have found.
Red berries! I do love
red berries."
She eats until she is full.
"We can call this Meg's
Berry Place," says Ben.
"But now we
must go on."

Skipper, Bob and Meg
go along the path
to the Misty Hills.
Is Ben lost?
No, here he is with a
very sticky face!
"I have found a bees' nest
full of honey," he says.
"We can call it Ben's Honey
Place," says Bob.
"But now we
must go on."

The path goes up a hill.
The ground is hard and
full of rocks and stones.
"We are in the Misty Hills,"
says Ben. "There is the tall
pine tree. That is where
I saw the rainbow end.
That is where we have
to go to find the pot
of gold."

They go to the tall pine
tree and look for the
pot of gold.
"There is nothing up here,"
says Meg the magpie.
"Nothing down here,"
says Bob the beaver.
"Nothing here at all!"
says Skipper sadly.
Ben is sad too, but he
says, "Never
mind the gold . . .

... Bob has found a lovely pond to swim in.
Skipper has found a new log house to live in.
Meg has found lots of nice berries to eat.
I have found a store full of sweet honey.
We have all found our own pot of gold!"

They are all very happy.
They make a camp fire and
sit round it. They eat the
food from the picnic box.
"It is a long way home,"
says Ben, "but it was fun
to go to the end of the
rainbow!"
Do you think there is a
pot of gold at the end of
the rainbow?
Maybe there is.

Say these words again

little	brown
Mother	clouds
rainbow	story
picnic	things
beaver	chipmunk
wait	follow
magpie	swimming
lovely	sticky
where	nothing
misty	Hello